Grades K-4

FOCUS ON
ELEMENTARY

Biology

Teacher's Manual
3rd Edition

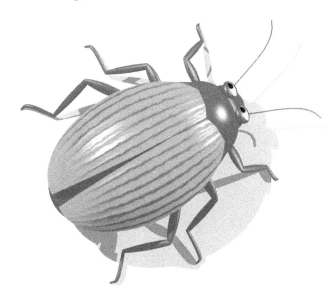

Rebecca W. Keller, PhD

Real Science-4-Kids

Cover design: David Keller
Opening page: David Keller, Rebecca W. Keller, PhD

Copyright © 2019 Gravitas Publications, Inc.

All rights reserved. No part of this publication may be reproduced, stored in a retrieval system, or transmitted, in any form or by any means, electronic, mechanical, photocopying, recording, or otherwise, without prior written permission from the publisher. No part of this book may be reproduced in any manner whatsoever without written permission.

Focus On Elementary Biology Teacher's Manual—3rd Edition
ISBN 978-1-941181-35-5

Published by Gravitas Publications Inc.
www.gravitaspublications.com
www.realscience4kids.com

A Note From the Author

This curriculum is designed to provide an introduction to biology for students in the elementary level grades. *Focus On Elementary Biology—3rd Edition* is intended to be used as the first step in developing a framework for the study of real scientific concepts and terminology in biology. This *Teacher's Manual* will help you guide students through the series of experiments in the *Laboratory Notebook*. These experiments will help the students develop the skills needed for the first step in the scientific method — making good observations.

There are several sections in each chapter. The section called *Observe It* helps the students explore how to make good observations. The *Think About It* section provides questions for the students to think about and use to make further observations. In every chapter there is a *What Did You Discover?* section that gives the students an opportunity to summarize the observations they have made. A section called *Why?* provides a short explanation of what students may or may not have observed. And finally, in each chapter there is a section called *Just For Fun* that contains an additional activity.

The experiments take up to 1 hour. The materials needed for each experiment are listed on the next page and also at the beginning of each experiment.

Enjoy!

Rebecca W. Keller, PhD

Materials at a Glance

Experiment 1	Experiment 3	Experiment 4	Experiment 5	Experiment 6
non-living object to observe (such as a rock or piece of wood) living thing to observe (such as an ant, frog, bird, cat, or dog) colored pencils	cotton balls rubber ball tennis ball banana apple rocks Legos other objects colored pencils	internet access and/or reference books colored pencils	milk, .25 l (1 cup) plain yogurt, .5 liter (2 cups) fork spoon cups or small bowls (several) food items such as honey, berries, chopped fruit or vegetables, spices, herbs, cocoa, chocolate chips, etc. (*Just For Fun* section)	microscope with a 10x or 20x objective lens (see the following How to Buy a Microscope section) plastic microscope slides[1] eye dropper pond water or protozoa kit[1] Protists (protozoa) can also be observed in hay water. To make hay water, cover a clump of dry hay with water and let it stand for several days at room temperature. Add water as needed

Experiment 2
magnifying glass colored pencils

Experiment 7	Experiment 8	Experiment 9	Experiment 10	Experiment 11
(see Experiment 6) small piece of chocolate **Optional** baker's yeast Eosin Y stain[2] distilled water	6-8 sealable plastic bags waterproof disposable gloves piece of newspaper or plastic 2 pieces of fruit 2-3 pieces of bread (works best if bread does not have preservatives) marking pen water **Optional** colored pencils	notebook or drawing pad with blank pages (not ruled) to make a nature journal pencil colored pencils **Optional** camera and printer tape backpack snack and bottle of water	2 small houseplants of the same kind and size 2 more small houseplants of the same kind and size water measuring cup closet or cardboard box colored pencils	2-4 white carnations 1 or more other white flowers (rose, lily, etc.) 2-3 small jars food coloring water tape knife colored pencils **Optional** magnifying glass

[1] As of this writing, the following materials are available from Home Science Tools, www.hometrainingtools.com: plastic microscope slides, MS-SLIDSPL or MS-SLPL144, Basic Protozoa Set, LD-PROBASC

[2] Eosin Y stain, CH-EOSIN (Home Science Tools)

Experiment 12	Experiment 13	Experiment 14	Experiment 15	Experiment 16
1-2 small clear glass jars 2 or more dried beans (white, pinto, soldier, etc.) 2 or more additional dried beans (different kind) or other seeds absorbent white paper scissors knife plastic wrap clear tape rubber band water **Optional** magnifying glass	student's field notebook pencil, pen colored pencils **Optional** camera and printer tape backpack snack and bottle of water	large tray or plastic box, at least .3 m (1 ft.) on each side, and cover garden dirt (with lots of organic material) spoon or garden trowel 12 snails/slugs and/or 20–40 worms [3] holding box for the snails/worms to keep them moist and dark water experimental snail and worm barriers. Set the amount you are going to use in an open container in the sun for a few days. table or rock salt plus three of the following: cinnamon baking soda black pepper cornstarch flour borax an active anthill	butterfly kit small cage Butterfly kits can be purchased from a variety of different sources, such as: Home Science Tools: www.hometrainingtools.com Insect Lore: www.insectlore.com	tadpole kit (or tadpoles or frog eggs collected locally) A tadpole kit can be purchased from Home Science Tools: www.hometrainingtools.com. aquarium water tadpole food

[3] Look for online or local sources of snails and/or earthworms. Or you and your students may be able to collect them yourselves.

Materials: Quantities Needed for All Experiments

Equipment	Materials	Materials (continued)
aquarium cage, small cup, measuring cups or small bowls (several) eye dropper fork jars, 2-3 small, clear glass knife Legos magnifying glass microscope with a 10x or 20x objective lens[1] scissors spoon spoon or garden trowel tray or plastic box, large, at least .3 m (1 ft.) on each side, and cover **Optional** camera and printer magnifying glass camera backpack	ball, rubber ball, tennis box for snails/worms to keep them moist and dark butterfly kit[2] carnations, 2-4 white cotton balls dirt, garden (with lots of organic material) flowers (rose, lily, etc.), white, 1 or more (not carnations) food coloring gloves, waterproof, disposable houseplants, 2 small - same kind and size houseplants, 2 additional, small - same kind and size living thing to observe (such as an ant, frog, bird, cat, or dog) microscope slides, plastic[2] newspaper or plastic, 1 piece notebook or drawing pad with blank pages (not ruled) non-living object to observe (such as a rock or piece of wood)	table or rock salt plus three of the following: cinnamon, baking soda, black pepper, cornstarch, flour, borax tadpole food tadpole kit (or tadpoles or frog eggs collected locally)[2] tape tape, clear water **Optional** Eosin Y stain[2] water, distilled

Foods		Other
apple banana beans, dried (white, pinto, soldier, etc.), 2 or more beans, dried (different from above) or other seeds, 2 or more bread, 2-3 pieces (best without preservatives) chocolate, small piece food items such as honey, berries, chopped fruit or vegetables, spices, herbs, cocoa, chocolate chips, etc. fruit, 2 pieces milk, .25 l (1 cup) yogurt, plain, .5 liter (2 cups) **Optional** baker's yeast snack and bottle of water	objects, misc. paper, absorbent white pen pen, marking pencil pencils, colored plastic bags, sealable, 6-8 plastic wrap pond water or protozoa kit protists (protozoa)[2] rocks rubber band snail and worm barriers, student choice of materials snails/slugs, 12, and/or 20–40 worms[3]	anthill, active closet or cardboard box internet access and/or reference books

[1] See the following *How to Buy a Microscope* section for recommendations.

[2] As of this writing, the following materials are available from Home Science Tools, www.hometrainingtools.com:
Butterfly kit (can also be purchased from Insect Lore: www.insectlore.com)
Eosin Y stain, CH-EOSIN
Plastic microscope slides, MS-SLIDSPL or MS-SLPL144
Basic Protozoa Set, LD-PROBASC
Tadpole kit

[3] Look for online or local sources of snails and/or earthworms. Or you and your students may be able to collect them.

How to Buy a Microscope

What to Look For

- A metal mechanical stage.
- A metal body painted with a resistant finish.
- DIN Achromatic Glass objective lenses at 4X, 10X, 40X (a 100X lens is optional but recommended).
- A focusable condenser (lens that focuses the light on the sample).
- Metal gears and screws with ball bearings for movable parts.
- Monocular (single tube) "wide field" ocular lens.
- Fluorescent lighting with an iris diaphragm.

Price Range

$50-$150: Not recommended: These microscopes do not have the best construction or parts and are often made of plastic. These microscopes will cause frustration, discouraging students.

$150-$350: A good quality standard student microscope can be found in this price range. We recommend Great Scopes for a solid student microscope with the best parts and optics in this price range. http://www.greatscopes.com

Above $350: There are many higher end microscopes that can be purchased, but for most students these are too much microscope for their needs. However, if you have a child who is really interested in microscopy, wants to enter the medical or scientific profession, or may become a serious hobbyist, a higher end microscope would be a valuable asset.

Objective lenses: Magnification/Resolution/Field of View/Focal Length

The objective lenses are the most important parts of the microscope. An objective lens not only magnifies the sample, but also determines the resolution. However, higher powered objective lenses with better resolution have a smaller field of view and a shorter focal length.

The resolution and working distance (focal length) of a lens is determined by its numerical aperture (NA). Following is a list of magnifications, numerical aperture, and working distance for some common achromatic objective lenses.

How to Buy a Microscope (Continued)

Magnification	Numerical Aperture	Working Distance (mm)
4X	0.10	30.00
10X	0.25	6.10
20X	0.40	2.10
40X	0.65	0.65
60X	0.80	0.30
100X (oil)	1.25	0.18

You can see as the magnification increases the numerical aperture increases (which means the resolution increases) and the working distance decreases.

Choosing the right lens for the right sample is part of the art of microscopy.

Most student projects can be achieved with a 40X objective, however a 100X objective lens can be added to make observing bacteria and small cell structures possible.

Below is a general chart showing the recommended objective lens to use for different types of samples.

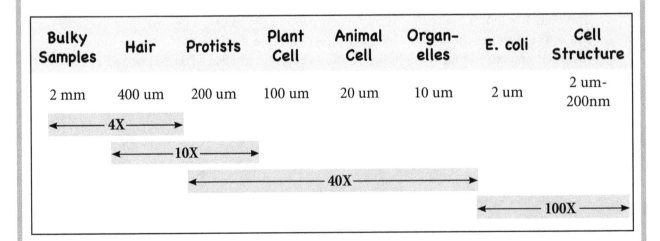

Contents

Experiment 1

What Is Life?

Materials Needed

- non-living object to observe, such as a rock or piece of wood
- living thing to observe, such as an ant, frog, bird, cat, or dog
- colored pencils

Objectives

In this experiment students will explore the differences between living and non-living things.

The objectives of this lesson are for students to:

- Observe features of living and non-living things.
- Think about the definition of life.

Experiment

I. Think About It

Read this section of the *Laboratory Notebook* with your students.

❶-❹ Help the students think about and answer the questions in this section. There are no right answers for these questions. Just allow the students to explore their own ideas about life and non-life.

II. Observe It

Read this section of the *Laboratory Notebook* with your students.

Help your students find a living thing and a non-living thing to observe. Have them write the name of each item in the space provided. In one column they will list or draw their observations for the living thing and in the other column their observations for the non-living thing.

Help them explore each item by asking the following questions.

- *Can the item move?*
- *Does the item breathe?*
- *Does the item consume food?*
- *Can the item reproduce itself?*

In the space provided have the students write or draw what they see.

III. What Did You Discover?

Read the questions with your students.

❶-❸ Have the students answer the questions. These can be answered orally or in writing. There are no right answers, and their answers will depend on what they actually observed.

IV. Why?

Read this section of the *Laboratory Notebook* with your students.

Discuss any questions that might come up.

V. Just For Fun

Read this section of the *Laboratory Notebook* with your students.

Have the students imagine what life on another planet might look like. Help them think about what characteristics they might include, such as how the creatures would move, what sort of appendages they would have and how many, their skin or fur color, the environment they'd live in, etc.

Have them write about and/or draw their imaginary living things. They can assign a name to the planet and name their creatures.

Experiment 2

Taking Notes

Materials Needed
- magnifying glass
- colored pencils

Objectives

In this experiment, students will explore how to use their five senses and basic tools to make good observations.

The objectives of this lesson are for students to:

- Observe both natural and man-made objects.
- Use a simple tool to make better observations.

Experiment

I. Think About It

Read this section of the *Laboratory Notebook* with your students.

Have the students think about how making good observations is important for studying biology. Have them explore how the natural world is both predictable and unpredictable and how plants and animals can react to the environment in both expected and unexpected ways (e.g., a cat may usually chase a mouse, but a cat might also just watch the mouse move and choose not to chase it).

Explore open inquiry with the following:

- *What does an ant look like? What color, shape, and size is it?*

- *What do you think is inside a tree? What does it look like? What color is the inside? Do you think there are several colors or just one?*

- *What happens when a cat jumps on a wall? How does it move its back legs? Does it use its front legs?*

- *What is the shape of a bird wing? Are all bird wings the same shape and size? Why or why not?*

Have the students think about these questions. Then have them come up with five of their own biology questions. There are five boxes provided in the *Laboratory Notebook* for their questions. Have the students write each question in the gray part of a box and then in the area below the question, write or draw their ideas about possible answers. There are no right answers to their questions. Encourage the students to use their imagination.

II. Observe It

Read this section of the *Laboratory Notebook* with your students.

Have the students take their *Laboratory Notebook,* pen or pencil, and a magnifying glass and go outside. They are not to use any type of electronic device to record their observations. They are also not to use a cellphone during this time. Using the five senses in doing science is a skill that needs to be developed before adding the use of technological aids. Have the students sit quietly for 10 minutes or so and just observe the smells, colors, sounds, and textures of the space surrounding them. Encourage them to use the magnifying glass to view any details they find interesting.

In the boxes provided in the *Laboratory Notebook,* have the students record what they see, hear, smell, and touch in the space around them. If they are sitting on the ground with dirt or grass, have them record what kind of ground they're on. If they are sitting on a bench or chair, have them record this. Have them note which of the items they observe are natural and which items are man-made.

III. What Did You Discover?

Read this section of the *Laboratory Notebook* with your students.

❶-❼ Have the students refer to their notes in the *Observe It* section and answer the questions. These can be answered orally or in writing. Again, there are no right answers and their answers will depend on what they actually observed.

IV. Why?

Read this section of the *Laboratory Notebook* with your students.

Discuss any questions that might come up.

V. Just For Fun

Read this section of the *Laboratory Notebook* with your students.

Have the students repeat this exploration in a place they have never visited. Take them to a new park or outdoor space. Or you can take them to a museum, library, ice cream parlor, or other location. Have them record what they see, smell, and hear.

Experiment 3

Where Does It Go?

Materials Needed

- cotton balls
- rubber ball
- tennis ball
- banana
- apple
- rocks
- Legos
- other objects
- colored pencils

Objectives

In this experiment the students will try to sort objects into different groups according to their characteristics.

The objectives of this lesson are:

- To help students understand that there are different ways to sort objects.
- To have students develop a vocabulary to describe the objects they observe.

Experiment

I. Observe It

In this section the students will make careful observations for each of the objects they have collected.

Read this section of the *Laboratory Notebook* with your students.

❶ Help the students collect objects to observe.

❷ Put the objects on a table and have the students look carefully at each item.

Help them observe different details such as size, color, shape, and texture for each item. Use questions to help them describe the object.

- *What color is a cotton ball?*
- *What color is a banana?*
- *What is the shape of a cotton ball?*
- *What is the shape of a rock?*
- *How would you describe the surface of a tennis ball?*

❸ Encourage students to use both words and pictures to describe each object. Have them use as many different describing words as possible for each item. Their answers may look something like this:

(Answers will vary.)

cotton ball

____*fuzzy*____   ____*round*____   ____*soft*____   ____*white*____

_____   _____   _____   _____

_____   _____   _____   _____

```
┌─────────────────────────────────────────────────────┐
│                                                       │
│                                                       │
│                                                       │
│                                                       │
└─────────────────────────────────────────────────────┘
```

tennis ball

____*fuzzy*____   ____*round*____   ____*hard*____   ____*yellow*____

_____   _____   _____   _____

_____   _____   _____   _____

```
┌─────────────────────────────────────────────────────┐
│                                                       │
│                                                       │
│                                                       │
└─────────────────────────────────────────────────────┘
```

(Answers will vary.)

rock

hard	gray	smooth	heavy

building block

square	hard	blue	plastic

II. Think About It

Read this section of the *Laboratory Notebook* with your students.

❶ Have the students look at the different objects and the different ways they have described the objects. Help them think about how they might group the objects according to their descriptions.

❷ Have the students think of five different groups and then write the names of the groups in the gray boxes. Next, have them sort the objects they have collected into the different groups. Each object can only go into **ONE** group.

Their answers may look something like this:

(Answers will vary.)				
round	yellow	small	hard	white
tennis ball	banana	rock	block	cotton ball
	apple		rubber ball	

❸-❹ Help the students notice that some items can fit into more than one group. For example, if they chose the groups round and yellow, a tennis ball can fit into both groups. Have the students think about how they might rearrange the groups, picking different items that go into each group. They can re-sort their items into the groups they've already chosen, or they can pick new groups.

Help them notice features that are similar and different between the objects by asking questions such as:

- *Is a rubber ball larger or smaller than a cotton ball?*

- *Is a rubber ball harder or softer than a cotton ball?*

- *Is a rock like a banana? Why or why not?*

- *Is a tennis ball similar to a banana? Why or why not?*

There are no "right" answers, so encourage the students to think about all the different ways they may want to sort the items.

III. What Did You Discover?

Read the questions with your students.

❶-❹ The questions can be answered verbally or in writing, depending on the writing ability of the student. With these questions, help the students think about their observations. Again, there are no "right" answers to these questions, and it is important for the students to write or discuss what they actually observed.

IV. Why?

Read this section of the *Laboratory Notebook* with your students.

It is important for students to understand that science is often a dynamic endeavor, and the "answers" that science provides can sometimes change. The identification and grouping of living things can be fairly complicated, and determining exactly which group a living thing belongs to is not trivial. There are different criteria used to group living things. Most living things are first grouped according to the types of cells they have — plant cells, animal cells, bacterial cells, etc. Once the organism is grouped according to cell type, then the scientist looks for other features to use in categorizing the organism.

V. Just For Fun

Read this section of the *Laboratory* with your students.

Help the students think about how they would categorize the new creature according to the features and groups given. There are no right or wrong answers in this section.

Encourage students to use their imagination in creating this new creature.

Experiment 4

What Do You Need?

Materials Needed

- internet access and/or reference books
- colored pencils

Objectives

In this experiment, students will explore different jobs their parents do in the home. They will also explore the steps it takes to bring a single tool into the house so that a parent can do their job. This will help students understand how a cell has many different parts that rely on each other and work together to allow the cell to live.

The objectives of this lesson are to help students:

- Observe some of the many different jobs needed to run a household.
- Understand how all of the jobs their parents do are connected to other jobs performed by other people.
- Understand how different parts of a cell work together and perform different functions.

Experiment

I. Observe It

Read this section of the *Laboratory Notebook* with the students.

❶ Have students follow their parent around and observe the jobs that are done. You might want to pick a day where the students can observe many different jobs, such as doing laundry, cooking a meal, washing the dishes, repairing a broken door, hanging a picture, cleaning the yard, or mowing the lawn.

Have the students bring their *Laboratory Notebook* with them as they observe their parent so they can record several jobs as they observe them being done. Their answers may look something like this:

(Answers will vary.)

Job	*cooking breakfast*
Job	*fixing the broken stove*
Job	*planting the garden*

❷ Have the students pick one of the jobs on their list. Have them think about and then write down or draw all of the items needed to do that job. Their answers may look something like this:

(Answers will vary.)

Job cooking breakfast	
Items Needed	
eggs	bowl
whisk	frying pan
butter	salt
pepper	green chili (for NM residents)

❸ Have your students draw a picture of the person doing the selected job. Have them include the tools that would be used to do the job.

❹ Have the students pick one of the tools from Step ❸ and draw it in detail in the space provided.

II. Think About it

Read this section of the *Laboratory Notebook* with your students.

❶-❻ Have the students answer the questions about the item they have selected. They may not be able to answer the questions exactly (they may not know exactly where the bowl or the whisk was purchased). Help them come up with general answers if needed ("grocery store" or "hardware store" is enough of a description).

Their answers may look something like this:

❶ **What is the item?**

whisk

❷ **Where did the item come from?**

grocery store

❸ **How did the item get there?**

on a truck

❹ **Who made the item?**

the whisk factory

❺ **What is the item made of?**

steel

❻ **Where does the material that makes the item come from?**

from iron ore

III. What Did You Discover?

Read this section of the *Laboratory Notebook* with your students.

❶-❻ Guide the students in answering the questions in this section. Help them think about all of the items people, including their parents, use to do different jobs. Have them think about all of the people it takes to make the items their parents use to do a job.

IV. Why?

Read this section with your students.

This experiment helps students have a better understanding of the many jobs people do and how many items are needed for them to be able to do those jobs. Help the students connect what they observed in this experiment with what goes on inside a cell. Help them see that a cell operates in a way that is similar to a city.

In order for someone to have a tool to do a job in a house, that tool needs to come from other people in other cities doing different jobs. Explain that there are "jobs" that proteins do inside cells so that the cells can live. Proteins inside the cells do these "jobs." In order for a protein to do its job, it depends on other proteins to do their jobs. For example, for a protein to move molecules from one place to another, other proteins are required to make the molecules that are to be moved.

Help the students see that inside a cell there is a very sophisticated network of proteins and other molecules that do the different jobs that make it possible for the cell to live.

V. Just For Fun

Read this section with your students.

Have the students select an item to observe. Guide their observations of the materials contained in the object they choose.

By looking up some of the ways materials, such as steel, are made, the students will gain a better understanding of how many people it takes to produce an item, such as a cooking whisk. Help the students search the internet or look at reference books to find the information.

Experiment 5

Yummy Yogurt

Materials Needed

- .25 liter (1 cup) regular milk
- .5 liter (2 cups) plain yogurt
- fork
- spoon
- several cups or small bowls
- food items such as honey, berries, chopped fruit or vegetables, spices, herbs, cocoa, chocolate chips, etc. (see *Just For Fun* section)

Objectives

In this experiment, students will examine the differences between yogurt and milk.

The objectives of this lesson are for students to:

- Make comparisons, observing differences and similarities.
- Examine how bacterial cultures change the consistency of milk.

Experiment

I. Think About It

Read this section of the *Laboratory Notebook* with your students.

Have the students think about bacteria and how bacteria live in many different places. ***Before having the students look at the yogurt and milk,*** help them think about what the differences between yogurt and regular milk might be. Guide their inquiry with questions such as the following:

- *What color do you think milk is?*

- *What color do you think yogurt is?*

- *Do you think yogurt tastes different from milk? If so, what do you think the difference in taste would be?*

- *Do you think you can you eat yogurt with a fork? Why or why not?*

- *Do you think you can you eat milk with a fork? Why or why not.*

There are no right answers for these questions. Just allow the students to explore their own ideas about the differences between yogurt and milk.

II. Observe It

Read this section of the *Laboratory Notebook* with your students.

Provide about .25 liter (1 cup) of milk and .25 liter (1 cup) of yogurt to the students. Have them observe the color, smell, taste, and consistency of each. Have them use a fork, a spoon, and their fingers to test the consistency.

Help students record their observations in the columns provided in their *Laboratory Notebook*.

III. What Did You Discover?

Read the questions with your students.

❶-❹ Have the students answer the questions. These can be answered orally or in writing, depending on the writing ability of the student. Again, there are no right answers, and their answers will depend on what they actually observed.

IV. Why?

Read this section of the *Laboratory Notebook* with your students.

Discuss any questions that might come up.

V. Just For Fun

Read this section of the *Laboratory Notebook)* with your students.

Have the students think about what foods they might add to yogurt to change its flavor, color, texture, and/or smell. Have them look around the kitchen to find some food items that look interesting to them. The objective is for students to try different mixtures and make observations about the outcomes. Some of their ideas may result in mixtures that you know won't taste good, but let them try these anyway.

Help the students mix their chosen food item into a small portion of yogurt and then taste it. Have them record their observations.

Guide the students' inquiry by asking questions about what they observe.

Experiment 6

Little Creatures Move

Materials Needed

- microscope with a 10x or 20x objective lens (look online for sources such as Great Scopes or Carolina Biological Supply)
- plastic microscope slides
- eye dropper
- pond water or protozoa kit

Protists (protozoa) can also be observed in hay water. To make hay water, cover a clump of dry hay with water and let it stand for several days at room temperature. Add water as needed.

As of this writing, the following materials are available from Home Science Tools, www.hometrainingtools.com:

- plastic microscope slides, MS-SLIDSPL or MS-SLPL144
- Basic Protozoa Set, LD-PROBASC

Objectives

In this unit students will look at pond water, hay water, or a protozoa kit to observe how protists (protozoa) move.

The objectives of this lesson are for students to:

- Make careful observations of protists moving.
- Practice using a microscope.

Experiment

I. Think About It

Read this section of the *Laboratory Notebook* with your students.

The students have read about how protists move. Now have them think about what movement for a protist might look like and what looking at pond water through a microscope might show. Help them explore their ideas with questions such as:

- *What do you think pond water looks like?*
- *Will you see moving creatures?*
- *Do you think you will be able to tell if they are moving? How?*
- *Do you think you will see them rolling or twisting?*
- *Do you think they will swim fast or slow? Straight or in a circle?*
- *What else do you think you might observe in pond water?*

Have them draw what they think they will see when they look at pond water through a microscope. There are no right answers—just let students explore their ideas.

II. Observe It

Read this section of the *Laboratory Notebook* with your students.

This is mainly an observational experiment.

❶ a) Help the students set up the microscope. Placing the microscope on a flat, firm surface will make it easier to use.

b) Help the students put a drop of protozoa water (or pond water or hay water) on a plastic slide.

c) Help the students carefully place the slide in the microscope.

d) Help the students look through the eyepiece at the water on the slide.

It may take several tries before protists can be observed. Help students repeat setting up the slide with samples as many times as necessary.

It is important for students to practice observing as many different details as possible. Have them draw their observations.

❷-❺ There are several drawing frames in the *Laboratory Notebook* for students to fill in with drawings of the different features they observe in the pond water. Encourage them to spend plenty of time looking at all the different features they observe. You can encourage them to stay at the microscope by engaging them with questions such as:

- *What kind of protist do you think you are seeing?*

- *Is it moving fast or slowly? Can you see it spin?*

- *How does it stop? Can it move backwards?*

- *Do you see an amoeba?*

- *How fast does an amoeba move?*

❻-❼ Have students compare some of the protists they are observing. They are asked to make comparisons between different protists of the same kind (two paramecia, for example) and protists of different kinds (possibly a paramecium and an amoeba).

III. What Did You Discover?

Read this section of the *Laboratory Notebook* with your students.

Have the students answer the questions about the protists they observed. Encourage them to refer to their notes in the *Observe It* section and summarize their answers based on their observations. They should have been able to see different protists moving in different ways. Have them explain what their favorite protist was and why. Help them notice any differences between what they thought they would observe and what they actually observed.

IV. Why?

Read this section of the *Laboratory Notebook* with your students.

There are many different kinds of protists. Depending on what your students used for protozoa water, they should have been able to observe at least two different kinds of protists.

Protists move like sophisticated little machines. They roll and spin, stop and start, move forward, and back up. Explain to the students how remarkable protists are since they are made with only one cell yet can do so many different things.

V. Just For Fun

Have the students put some saliva on a slide and look at it under the microscope to see if they can find any organisms. Have them record their results.

Experiment 7

Little Creatures Eat

Materials Needed

- microscope with a 10X or 20x objective lens (look online for sources such as Great Scopes or Carolina Biological Supply)
- plastic microscope slides
- eye dropper
- pond water or protozoa kit
- small piece of chocolate

Optional

- baker's yeast
- Eosin Y stain
- distilled water

Protists (protozoa) can also be observed in hay water. To make hay water, cover a clump of dry hay with water, and let it stand for several days at room temperature. Add water as needed.

As of this writing, the following materials are available from Home Science Tools, www.hometrainingtools.com:

- plastic microscope slides, MS-SLIDSPL or MS-SLPL144
- Basic Protozoa Set, LD-PROBASC
- Eosin Y stain, CH-EOSIN

Objectives

In this unit students will look at pond water, hay water, or water from a protozoa kit to observe how protists (protozoa) eat.

The objectives of this lesson are for students to:

- Make careful observations of protists eating.
- Practice using a microscope.

Experiment

In this experiment students will focus on protists that are eating. If pond water or hay water is being used, there should be plenty of food for the protists to eat.

Baker's yeast stained with Eosin Y can be added to any of the kinds of protozoa water. The Eosin Y stained yeast will be ingested by the protists. Once ingested, the red stained yeast will turn blue. It may take some time for this observation.

To make baker's yeast and Eosin Y stain:

- Add 5 milliliters (one teaspoon) of dried yeast to 120 milliliters (1/2 cup) of distilled water. Allow it to dissolve. Let the mixture sit for a few minutes, then add one dropper of Eosin Y to one dropper of the baker's yeast solution and let sit for a few minutes.
- Look at a droplet of the mixture under the microscope. You should be able to see individual yeast cells that are stained red.

I. Think About It

Read this section of the *Laboratory Notebook* with your students.

The students have read about how protists eat. Have them first think about what it might look like for a protist to eat. Help them explore their ideas with questions such as:

- *How do you think a paramecium eats?*
- *Do you think you can watch it eat?*
- *Do you think you can tell if the food is going inside?*
- *How do you think an amoeba eats?*
- *Do you think an amoeba can eat fast moving food? Why or why not?*
- *What else do you think you might see as the protists eat?*

Have the students draw what they think they will observe through the microscope as they watch protists eat.

II. Observe It

Read this section of the *Laboratory Notebook* with your students.

❶ **a)** Help the students place a small droplet of the protozoa solution onto a microscope slide.

b) If using Eosin Y stained baker's yeast, have the students add a droplet of the stained baker's yeast to the protozoa water on the slide.

c) Help the students carefully place the slide in the microscope.

d) Have the students look through the eyepiece at the protozoa water on the slide.

(You may also position the slide correctly in the microscope and then add the liquids to it.)

It is important for students to practice observing as many different details as possible. Have them draw what they observe.

❷-❺ There are several drawing frames in the *Laboratory Notebook* for students to fill in with drawings of their observations of protists eating. Encourage the students to spend plenty of time looking at all the different features they observe. You can encourage them to stay at the microscope by engaging them with questions such as:

- *What kind of protist do you think you are seeing?*

- *Is it eating?*

- *Can you tell what it is eating?*

- *Can you tell if the protist is eating another protist or something else?*

- *How fast does it eat?*

❻-❼ Have the students compare some of the protists they are observing. They can make comparisons between different protists of the same kind (two paramecia, for example) and protists of different kinds (possibly a paramecium and an amoeba).

III. What Did You Discover?

Read this section of the *Laboratory Notebook* with your students.

Have students answer the questions about the protists they observed. Encourage them to summarize their answers based on their observations. They should have been able to see different protists eating. Have them explain what their favorite protist was, how it was eating, and why it was their favorite. Help them notice any differences between what they thought they would observe and what they actually observed.

IV. Why?

Read this section of the *Laboratory Notebook* with your students.

Different protists eat in different ways. Your students may or may not have been able to observe the protists eating. Explain to them that watching protists eat is sometimes like watching the tigers eat at the zoo. They may not be hungry. Repeat the experiment at a different time if your student was not able to observe protists eating.

V. Just For Fun

Help the students put a tiny piece of chocolate on the slide with the protozoa water. Have them look through the microscope to see if the protozoa will eat chocolate. Have them record their observations in the space provided.

Experiment 8

Oldy Moldy

Materials Needed

- 6-8 sealable plastic bags
- 2 pairs waterproof disposable gloves
- 2 or more pieces of newspaper or plastic
- 2 pieces of fruit
- 2-3 pieces of bread (will mold more quickly if it does not have preservatives)
- marking pen
- water

Optional

- colored pencils

Objectives

In this experiment, students will explore whether a mold that grows on fruit will grow on bread.

The objectives of this lesson are for students to:

- Describe events that happen during an experiment.
- Develop explanations using observations.

Experiment

I. Think About It

Read this section of the *Laboratory Notebook* with your students.

Have the students think about molds, mushrooms, and yeast they may have observed. Explore open inquiry with questions such as the following:

- *Have you ever seen a mushroom? What did it look like?*

- *Have you seen mushrooms that look different from each other? What did they look like?*

- *Have you ever seen mold? Where was it? What did it look like?*

- *Have you ever observed mold on fruit? Or mold on food that is in the refrigerator? Did it all look the same?*

- *Have you ever eaten bleu cheese? What did it taste like? What did it look like? Why do you think it is called bleu?*

Have the students answer the questions in this section of the *Laboratory Notebook*. There are no right answers to these questions.

II. Observe It

Read this section of the *Laboratory Notebook* with your students.

❶ Molds require moisture and warm room temperatures to grow quickly and thrive. Help the students find a warm spot in the kitchen for their experiment and have them put down some newspaper or plastic for the fruit to sit on.

Have the students cut the piece of fruit in half or do it for them. This will reduce handling of the moldy fruit later in the experiment. Have them let the fruit sit for several days until it is getting moldy. The fruit can be covered with a piece of newspaper or plastic to prevent the mold spores from scattering to other areas..

❷ Once the fruit is moldy, have the students take 3 plastic bags and label them **Control**, **Moldy Fruit**, and **Moldy Fruit + Bread** along with the date.

❸ Have the students put 5 milliliters (1 teaspoon) of water in each of the bags. If this amount of water does not make the food moist, have them add more water at this time. The goal is for the food to be moist but not soggy and for the bag to remain sealed during the experiment. This experiment might take longer in a cooler environment than a warmer one.

❹-❽ Have the students put on waterproof disposable gloves to handle the moldy fruit. They will put a fresh piece of bread in the **Control** bag, one piece of moldy fruit in the **Moldy Fruit** bag, and the other piece of moldy fruit and a fresh piece of bread in the **Moldy Fruit + Bread** bag. Have them thoroughly seal each bag and leave the bags in a warm, out of the way area.

Fungi do not need much fresh air to grow because they do not photosynthesize. The air in the bag is sufficient for a few days of cellular respiration of molds, which are small and grow slowly. Sealing the bags keeps the mold spores from being blown away and spreading around the kitchen.

The molds that grow on foods are generally not found to be dangerous to inhale. But to be safe, have the students cover the work area and clean up thoroughly. **Do not let them open the bags at the end of the experiment**—just throw them away.

❾ Have the students check the bags daily for 3-7 days. In the chart provided, have them write or draw each day's observations of the contents of each bag. **Do not let them open the bags.**

❿ When the experiment is over have the students **throw everything away without opening the bags.**

The molds the students observe may be a combination of the molds introduced during the experiment and molds already present on the food. Some fruit molds can grow on other types of foods and some cannot. Some fruits have anti-fungal agents, either naturally or added to them; molds will not grow on these.

The colors can vary with the types of molds that appear.

III. What Did You Discover?

Read this section of the *Laboratory Notebook* with your students.

Have the students answer the questions. These can be answered orally or in writing. Again, there are no right answers, and their answers will depend on what they actually observed.

IV. Why?

Read this section of the *Laboratory Notebook* with your students.

Discuss any questions that might come up.

V. Just For Fun

Here students will reverse the experiment to determine if bread mold will grow on fruit. To do this, they will first grow the mold on the bread instead of the fruit. A clean piece of fruit will be the control.

This time students can create their own experiment. To help them come up with the steps needed, have them review the steps of the experiment they performed previously. Guide them to come up with the experiment summarized below.

To have the bread get moldy instead of drying out, have the students put it in a plastic bag with 5 ml (1 teaspoon) of water. To reduce handling of the moldy bread, students can either cut in half the piece of bread that is to get moldy or let 2 pieces of bread get moldy.

Once the bread is moldy, students can cut in half the fresh fruit to be tested. Then they will label the bags and put the moldy bread and fresh fruit in them. Have them wear disposable waterproof gloves to handle the moldy bread. They will have a bag labeled **Control** that will contain a piece of the fresh fruit, a bag labeled **Moldy Bread** will contain a piece of the moldy bread, and a bag labeled **Moldy Bread + Fruit** will contain a piece of the moldy bread and a piece of the fresh fruit. The bags should be sealed thoroughly.

Have them check the bags each day **without opening them** and write or draw their observations in the chart provided.

At the end of the experiment, have students thoroughly clean the work area and **throw away the bags without opening them.**

Experiment 9

Nature Walk:
Observing Plants

Materials Needed

- notebook or drawing pad with blank pages (not ruled) to make into a field notebook
- pencil
- colored pencils

Optional

- camera and printer
- tape
- backpack
- snack and bottle of water

Objectives

In this experiment, students will observe plants growing in their environment.

The objectives of this lesson are for students to:

- Explore the basic needs of plants—air, water, nutrients, temperature, and light.
- Examine different organisms in their environment.

Experiment

I. Think About It

Read this section of the *Laboratory Notebook* with your students.

Have the students think about plants they have already observed.

Explore open inquiry with questions such as the following:

- *What kinds of plants have you seen growing? Where were they growing?*
- *What kinds of plants have you eaten? Where do you think they came from?*
- *What features of plants have you observed?*
  (flowers, leaves, thorns etc.)
- *How do you think you can tell one kind of plant from another?*
- *How are plants different from rocks?*
- *Do you think you could put a plant in the soil anywhere and it would grow and be healthy? Why or why not?*

Have the students answer the questions in this section. There are no right answers.

II. Observe It

Read this section of the *Laboratory Notebook* with your students.

❶ For this experiment provide the students with a notebook or drawing pad that has blank pages. They will use it to make a field notebook.

Take your students on a nature walk and help them observe the plants around them. Students will need their notebook, a pencil, colored pencils, and a camera if one is available. They can take everything in a backpack along with a snack and a bottle of water.

❷ Have the students choose two or more plants to study closely.

❸ Have them notice the size, shape, color, texture, and other features of the plants. Encourage them to draw the plants they've chosen. They don't need to be able to draw the plant accurately; attempting to draw it will cause them to look more closely at the plant and observe more details than if they just photograph it.

❹ Have the students observe the environment in which the plants are living, and in their notebook write details such as temperature, available water, soil conditions, and amount of sunlight or shade.

❺ If a camera is available, have them photograph the plants and tape the photos in the notebook next to their drawings.

❻ Take the students on additional nature walks and have them record their observations in their field notebook.

III. What Did You Discover?

Have the students refer to their notes as they answer these questions. There are no right answers and their answers will depend on what they actually observed.

IV. Why?

Read this section of the *Laboratory Notebook* with your students.

Discuss any questions that might come up.

V. Just For Fun

Students are to add observations to their field notebook by choosing two or more plants to observe over a period of several months. It would be helpful to set up a schedule for students to make observations which they will record in their field notebook.

The students may continue to observe the plants they chose for the *Observe It* section, or they may select different ones. However, once they have chosen the plants, they should observe the same plants for several months, looking for any changes they undergo.

Students may enjoy using their field notebook to make notes and drawings about other things they observe in the plants' environment, such as animals, birds, insects, rocks, etc. Encourage them to draw and write freely in their field notebook.

Experiment 10

Who Needs Light?

Materials Needed

- 2 small houseplants of the same kind and size
- 2 more small houseplants of the same kind and size
- water
- measuring cup
- closet or cardboard box
- colored pencils

Objectives

In this unit students will observe what happens to a plant if it does not get sunlight.

The objectives of this lesson are:

- For students to make careful observations and to compare a plant grown with sunlight to one grown without sunlight.
- To introduce the concept of using a *control*.

A *control* is a tool scientists use to compare the specific effect that making a change has on an experiment. By comparing the plant that stays in the sunlight (the control) to a plant that does not get sunlight (the unknown), students can better observe the effect that the absence of sunlight will have on the plant. Without a control, it can be hard to know for certain what caused the observed changes.

Experiment

I. Think About It

Read this section of the *Laboratory Notebook* with your students.

❶ Have the students think about what things plants need to have in order to live. Some of the basic things plants need are sunlight, air, water, minerals, etc.

❷ Have the students answer the question that asks what they think will happen if a plant does not get any sunlight. This may seem obvious to the students, but help them think about the details. Use questions such as:

- *What do you think will happen to the leaves if there is no sunlight?*

- *What color do you think the leaves will turn?*

- *What do you think the leaves will feel like after a few days without sunlight? Firm or soft?*

- *How many days do you think it will take for the plant that is without sunlight to show some problems?*

- *What do you think will happen first?*

- *What do you think will happen last?*

II. Observe It

Read this section of the *Laboratory Notebook* with your students.

❶-❷ Have the students look carefully at the two plants.

❸ Help them find words to describe their plants in detail.

Have them notice anything different between the plants.

❹ Have them label one plant "**A**" and the other plant "**B**."

Have the students draw their plants. Drawing helps students make more detailed observations.

This step sets up the first part of the experiment. It is important for students to record, in as much detail as possible, the substances and conditions present when an experiment begins. This way, the changes that occur during the experiment can be more easily tracked.

❺-❻ Have the students place the plant labeled **A** in a sunny place and the plant labeled **B** in a dark place. A dark closet would work well, but a cardboard box could also be used as long as it does not let in any light.

❼ Have the students think about what they might observe and then record their ideas.

❽ Guide the students in coming up with a schedule for watering the plants on a regular basis and help them decide how much water to use each time. Have them measure the water each time they water the plants.

Have the students draw what has happened to the plants after one week. Help them observe any differences.

Depending on the type of plant you have selected, it may be several weeks before a significant difference is observed. Have the students observe the plants weekly and record any changes they observe.

III. What Did You Discover?

Read this section of the *Laboratory Notebook* with your students.

Based on their actual observations, have the students answer the questions about what happened to the two plants. Have them write about any significant differences they observed.

IV. Why?

Read this section of the *Laboratory Notebook* with your students.

Discuss what happens when a plant does not get enough sunlight to be able to make its own food. Also discuss how using a control helped in comparing normal plant growth in sunlight to abnormal plant growth with no sunlight. Help the students understand that by using a control, they can make direct comparisons between plants that are subject to two different conditions—sunlight or no sunlight. Explain to them that a control helped them to determine specifically what effect sunlight, or the lack of it, had on the plants, since the amount of exposure to sunlight was the only factor that was different between the two plants—everything else should have stayed the same.

V. Just For Fun

In this experiment students will take two houseplants of the same kind and size and water one but not the other. Both plants should be placed near each other so all the parameters of the experiment are the same except for how much water the plants get.

Have the students review the experiment they performed in the *Observe It* section. Help them think about what modifications they need to make to come up with the steps for this experiment. Ask questions such as the following:

- *What do you think will happen to the plants?*

- *Which steps of the experiment will stay the same? Which steps will you change?*

- *After what length of time do you think you will notice a change in the plants?*

- *How frequently will you make observations?*

- *Do you think both plants should be kept near each other? Why or why not?*

Space is provided for beginning and ending observations. Students can choose to use additional paper to record more observations.

Experiment 11

Thirsty Flowers

Materials Needed

- 2-4 white carnations
- 1 or more other white flowers (rose, lily, etc.)
- 2-3 small jars
- food coloring
- water
- tape
- knife
- colored pencils

Optional

- magnifying glass

Objectives

In this unit students will observe how water travels through a plant stem and a flower.

The objectives of this lesson are to have students:

- Make careful observations about how plants use their stems for "drinking" water.
- Compare what they think will happen to the flower to what they actually observe.

Experiment

I. Think About It

Read this section of the *Laboratory Notebook* with your students.

❶ Have the students think about what will happen to the flower of a carnation if they put the stem in colored water. Help them be as specific as possible. Use questions such as:

- *What do you think will happen to the flower if you put the stem in blue water? Why?*

- *Do you think all of the petals will change color? Why or why not?*

- *Do you think only some of the petals will change color? Why or why not?*

- *Do you think none of the petals will change color? Why or why not?*

- *How do you think the petals may change color? From the end to the center? Or from the center to the end? Why?*

- *Do you think you will be able to see the colored water in the stem? Why or why not?*

- *Do you think the green color of the stem will color the flower? Why or why not?*

- *If you add yellow coloring to the blue water, will the flower turn blue and yellow? Or some other color? Why?*

❷ Have the students draw a picture of what they think will happen, showing details.

II. Observe It

Read this section of the *Laboratory Notebook* with your students.

❶ Have the students carefully observe and draw a white carnation. Help them examine any fine details they find interesting.

❷ Take the carnation and split it in two (or have the students cut it) lengthwise.

Have the students draw the inside of the stem and flower.

❸ Put some water in one of the jars. Add several drops of food coloring, using enough to deeply color the water. You may need to adjust the amounts of water and food coloring. Too much water and too few drops of food coloring will make the dye too dilute, and the coloring of the petals won't be very dark.

Have the students place a carnation in the jar. Make sure the end of the stem is fully submerged in the colored water. You may need to have the students tape the side of the stem to the jar or prop the flower so it does not come out of the water.

Have the students draw the "start" of the experiment. Have them note details, such as how the carnation is fixed to the jar or if it is tilted or how well the stem is submerged.

Have them observe the carnation for the next several minutes. As they note changes, have them draw the flower and record the number of minutes that have passed. Four boxes have been provided for recording these observations. It may take many minutes before the petals of the carnation are fully colored. Have the students make as many observations as possible. Help them pay attention to how the petals are being colored—from the top, side, bottom and so on.

❹ Cut the stem open, or have the students do this, and have them observe the inside. A magnifying glass can be used. Guide their observations with questions such as:

- *Can you see the colored water traveling through the stem?*

- *Can you tell which part of the stem had the water traveling upward?*

- *Do you notice anything interesting about the stem? If so, describe it.*

III. What Did You Discover?

Read this section of the *Laboratory Notebook* with your students.

Have the students answer the questions about what they observed during this experiment. Help them think about the comparison between the way the carnation looked before and after it was put into the colored water.

IV. Why?

Read this section of the *Laboratory Notebook* with your students.

Discuss how the plant "drank" water from the jar. Tell the students that it is similar to how they drink liquid from a straw. When they put their mouth on the straw and suck in the air that is in the straw, liquid moves up from the bottom of their drink. A plant does essentially the same thing, except the "suction" comes from water evaporating from the leaves and petals.

If the students were able to observe differences inside the stem (such as parts of the stem that were light green, dark green, or white), explain to them that a stem has several different types of tissues. One of those tissues (called the xylem) draws water and nutrients up from the soil through the roots. Another type of tissue (called the phloem) pulls food back down through the stem to the roots and other parts of the plant. Tell them that only one type of tissue inside the stem draws the water up from the bottom of the jar, and the liquid will not drain back out again.

V. Just For Fun

Have students repeat the experiment using one or more different white flowers. Have them observe whether anything different happens.

Experiment 12

Growing Seeds

Materials Needed

- 1-2 small clear glass jars
- 2 or more dried beans (white, pinto, soldier, etc.)
- 2 or more dried beans of a different kind or 2 or more other seeds
- absorbent white paper
- scissors
- knife
- plastic wrap
- tape
- rubber band
- water

Optional

- magnifying glass

Objectives

In this unit students will observe how a seed grows into a plant.

The objectives of this lesson are for students to:

- Make careful observations about how a seed grows.
- Compare what they think will happen to what they actually observe.

Experiment

I. Think About It

Read this section of the *Laboratory Notebook* with your students.

❶ Have the students think about what will happen if they put a bean in a jar, add water, and let it sit for several days. Help them be as specific as possible. Direct their inquiry with questions such as:

- *What do you think will happen to a bean that gets water?*
- *Do you think the roots will come out first?*
- *Do you think the leaves will come out first?*
- *Do you think the bean will change color?*
- *What do you think might happen to the skin on the bean?*
- *How long do you think it will take for the bean to start to grow?*

Have them record their ideas.

❷ Have the students draw what they think will happen.

II. Observe It

Read this section of the *Laboratory Notebook* with your students.

❶ Have the students carefully observe and draw the outside of the bean. Help them examine any fine details they find interesting.

❷ Help the students split the bean lengthwise into two parts and then have them draw the inside of the bean, including any details they notice. A magnifying glass can be used while making the observations.

Guide the students in performing the following steps of the experiment.

❸   Take a clear glass jar and a piece of absorbent white paper. Cut a piece of the paper that is long enough to go all the way around the jar. Then wrap it around the inside of the jar.

❹   Place two dried beans between the paper and the jar. The paper should hold the beans against the side of the jar, but you may need to tape the beans to the jar if the paper doesn't hold them in place.

Make sure the beans are not touching the bottom of the jar but are placed about 6-12 mm (1/4-1/2 inch) above the bottom.

❺   Pour some water in the bottom of the jar so that the water contacts the absorbent paper but not the beans. (**Note:** *The beans will rot if they are in the water.*)

❻   Place plastic wrap on top of the jar and fasten it with a rubber band to seal the jar and prevent evaporation of the water.

❼   Have the students draw the start of the experiment. Have them note details, such as how the beans are oriented in the jar—up, down, sideways, etc.

❽   Have them observe the beans as they grows into plants. Beans generally begin to germinate in 5-7 days. It may take several weeks for the bean plants to fully develop. Have the students record all of their observations as they watch the beans grow. Have them record observations for each bean, comparing any similarities and differences between the beans.

Have the students check the water level frequently. It is important that the paper stay moist.

Allow the beans to fully sprout. Both the roots and leaves should be clearly visible. Have the students note the direction in which the roots grow and the direction in which the leaves grow.

If you wish to continue the experiment, you can have the students plant the seedlings and observe what happens. Do they become healthy plants? Why or why not?

III. What Did You Discover?

Read this section of the *Laboratory Notebook* with your students.

Have the students answer the questions about how the beans grew. Help them think about their observations and write summary statements about what they observed. Have them note whether or not the beans grew as they expected.

If the beans did not grow, guide the students in thinking about why this may have happened.

IV. Why?

Read this section of the *Laboratory Notebook* with your students.

Discuss the observations students made about how the beans grew. They should have noticed that the roots of the bean plant emerged first, followed by the leaves. They should also have observed that the roots grew down, toward the Earth, and the leaves grew up, toward the Sun.

Ask them how they think a plant "knows" in which direction to grow the roots and in which direction to grow the leaves. Explain that plant roots have molecules inside that tell roots to grow downward and that leaves have different molecules telling the leaves to grow upward toward the Sun.

V. Just For Fun

The students will repeat the experiment, this time using different seeds. They can use a different kind of dried bean seed, get seeds from the store, or save seeds from raw fruit or vegetables they eat. If they are saving their own seeds from food they eat, have them let the seeds dry before they begin the experiment to prevent the seeds from getting moldy. If they would like to experiment with several different seeds, they can put some different kinds of seeds in the same jar or use more than one jar.

Have the students record their observations. One box has been provided, and students can use additional pieces of paper if they choose.

Experiment 13

Nature Walk:
Observing Animals

Materials Needed

- student's field notebook
- pencil, pen
- colored pencils

Optional

- camera and printer
- tape
- backpack
- snack and bottle of water

Objectives

In this experiment students will observe animals in their environment.

The objectives of this lesson are for students to:

- Explore the basic needs of animals—air, water, and food.
- Examine different animals in the environment.

Experiment

I. Think About It

Read this section of the *Laboratory Notebook* with your students.

Have the students think about animals they have already observed. Explore open inquiry with questions such as the following:

- *What kinds of animals have you seen in your house, yard, and environment?*

- *What things have you seen animals eat?*

- *What kinds of animals have you eaten, if any?*

- *What features have you observed in animals? (hair, eyes, legs, etc.)*

- *In what different ways do animals move?*

- *Do you think animals can communicate with each other? Why or why not? If so, how?*

- *In what ways are animals different from plants?*

II. Observe It

Read this section of the *Laboratory Notebook* with your students.

In this experiment students will record observations about animals in their biologist's field notebook. Observations can be recorded as written notes, drawings, and/or photographs.

Take your students on a nature walk or to a zoo and help them observe the animals around them. Have them notice size, shape, color, and other features, such as type of hair, feathers, or scales, and shape of ears and tail, etc. Help them pick one or two animals to study closely. Encourage students to draw at least one of the animals they see. They will notice more features if they attempt to draw the animal than if they only take a photograph.

III. What Did You Discover?

Read this section of the *Laboratory Notebook* with your students.

Have the students refer to their field notebook as they answer the questions. There are no right answers and their answers will depend on what they actually observed.

IV. Why?

Read this section of the *Laboratory Notebook* with your students.
Discuss any questions that might come up.

V. Just For Fun

Students will continue to add their observations to their field notebook, observing animals over the course of several months to see how animals grow and change and how their activities differ with the seasons. Students can add more animals to observe.

Encourage students to look for features and behaviors they may not have noticed before. They may also see animals they did not notice previously. Drawing the animals is a good tool for making detailed observations.

Experiment 14

Red Light, Green Light

Materials Needed

- large tray or plastic box, at least .3 meter (1 ft) on each side
- something big enough to cover the tray
- garden dirt (lots of organic material is important for worms)
- spoon or garden trowel
- holding box for the snails/worms that keeps them moist and dark
- 12 snails/slugs and/or 20–40 worms
- water
- Experimental snail and worm barriers. If you can, set the amount of powder you are going to use in an open container in the sun for a few days.
- Use table or rock salt and choose three from the following list:
  cinnamon
  baking soda
  black pepper
  cornstarch
  flour
  borax
- an active anthill

Objectives

In this experiment, students will observe external cues that influence animal behavior.

The objectives of this lesson are for students to:

- Examine how animals detect external cues.
- Explore how an organism's environment influences its behavior.

Experiment

I. Think About It

Read this section of the *Laboratory Notebook* with your students.

Have the student think about animals they have already observed.

Explore open inquiry with questions such as the following:

- *What is an earthworm?*
- *What is a snail?*
- *How are they similar?*
- *How are they different?*
- *How do you think earthworms and snails would respond to a barrier that's put in their way?*
- *Do you think earthworms and snails will both respond to a barrier in a similar way? Why or why not?*

II. Observe It

Read this section of the *Laboratory Notebook* with your students.

You can use both snails and earthworms for this experiment, or you can choose one or the other. The experiment can also be done with slugs.

Snails are readily found in the late spring and summer months in many parts of the world. Earthworms can be ordered year-round in most parts of the United States, however, the availability in other countries will vary. Some investigators claim that European earthworms are hardier than red wigglers, but red wigglers are cheaper. If you plan to keep your worms inside and alive for more than a few days, look for advice. Worm-selling companies and other enthusiasts will share their knowledge on how to build and prepare a suitable habitat and how to feed and care for the worms. Worms can be kept for months on moist newspaper and fed kitchen scraps. They do not smell and will make compost for plants.

Be sure to protect the experiment from cold or heat. Cold will stop the subjects from moving, and heat will kill them. You could use direct sunlight to encourage snails to go in the right direction. While worms have no eyes but only light sensors scattered across their body, snails have primitive eyes. Snails are capable of climbing vertical surfaces and can even climb over a knife blade without injuring themselves.

❶ Help students put enough dirt in the plastic box or tray to completely cover the bottom.

❷ Have the students add some water to the dirt in one-half of the box, being careful to add only enough to make the dirt moist and not soggy. The dirt in the other half of the box needs to stay as dry as possible.

❸ Have students perform a control experiment by placing the subjects on the dry side of the box. Here, the snails/earthworms will be responding to conditions that are likely to happen in nature. It's expected that they will move from the dry area to the moist area. Have students record their observations.

❹-❿ Help students carefully move the subjects from the box with dirt to the holding box between each part of the experiment.

Students are to pour a line of one of the powders on top of the dirt and from one side of the box to the other, dividing the dry and moist areas. Before they use a different powder, have them carefully remove the old powder and put more dirt in the area they have dug out.

Have students use salt as one of the powders. The expected results are that a few worms may go into the salt barrier, while snails should not be willing to cross a barrier of salt. Salt draws moisture out of tissues, which is deadly to both of these creatures. When encountering salt, the snails start to foam. This is a defensive reaction that is not directly caused by the salt.

Snails are generally unwilling to cross any of the substances on the list except for flour and cornstarch.

When encountering substances such as cinnamon and pepper, snails merely pull in their tentacles and head off in another direction or hide inside their shells.

III. What Did You Discover?

Read this section of the *Laboratory Notebook* with your students.

Have the students refer to their experimental observations as they answer the questions. There are no right answers and their answers will depend on what they actually observed.

IV. Why?

Read this section of the *Laboratory Notebook* with your students.

Discuss any questions that might come up.

V. Just For Fun

In this section students will design their own experiment to see if there are barriers that ants will not cross. Have students review the steps in the snail/earthworm experiment and then write the steps for their own experiment based on those. Help them find an active anthill to use in this experiment. They can use the same substances as for the snail/earthworm experiment or they may want to choose different foods or nontoxic household substances.

Allow students to explore their ideas. There is no right answer to this experiment.

Experiment 15

Butterflies Flutter By

Materials Needed

- butterfly kit
- small cage

Butterfly kits can be purchased from a variety of different sources, such as:

Home Science Tools:
www.hometrainingtools.com

Insect Lore:
www.insectlore.com

Objectives

In this experiment students will observe a caterpillar turning into a butterfly.

The objectives of this lesson are for students to:

- Make careful observations of the metamorphosis of a butterfly.
- Learn about a life cycle.

Experiment

I. Think About It

Read this section of the *Laboratory Notebook* with your students.

❶ Have students think about how a butterfly got its name. Help them look up the origin of the butterfly name from a library or internet reference.

Have them make a drawing of how they think the butterfly got its name.

❷ Have the students think about how a caterpillar turns into a butterfly. Guide their exploration of their ideas with questions such as:

- *What do you think happens first when a caterpillar changes to a butterfly?*
- *What do you think happens next when a caterpillar changes to a butterfly?*
- *What do you think happens last when a caterpillar changes to a butterfly?*
- *Do you think you can watch the caterpillar in the chrysalis as it changes to a butterfly?*
- *What do you think the chrysalis is made of?*
- *What color do you think the chrysalis will be?*

Have the students make a drawing of how they think a caterpillar turns into a butterfly.

II. Observe It

Read this section of the *Laboratory Notebook* with your students.

Have the students:

- Follow the instructions to set up the butterfly kit.
- Make careful observations of the different stages of metamorphosis. If they are starting with a chrysalis rather than eggs, help them find pictures of butterfly eggs online or in the library.
- Draw the life cycle of the butterfly as they observe it.
- Write or draw any other interesting observations.

III. What Did You Discover?

Read this section of the *Laboratory Notebook* with your students.

Have students write summary statements of what they actually observed. They may have expected something different to happen, but encourage them to record what actually happened—even if the butterflies did not grow or the eggs or chrysalis died.

IV. Why?

Read this section of the *Laboratory Notebook* with your students.

Help the students understand that the life cycle of a butterfly is a very amazing process. Explain to them that if scientists did not make careful observations, they would not know that a caterpillar and a butterfly are the same creature and would not know about the life cycle of a butterfly.

Discuss the origin of the name *butterfly*.

Have the students discuss some reasons why they think scientists might not always be in agreement and why careful observations are important.

V. Just For Fun

Observing living things in their habitat is an important part of the study of biology. Help your students review this chapter in the *Student Textbook* and write down some features of arthropods in their field notebook. Have them bring their field notebook with them on a nature walk in a park, wooded area, or around the yard. Help them find arthropods in nature and guide them in identifying different stages in arthropod life cycles. Have them add notes and drawings about what they observe.

Experiment 16

Tadpoles To Frogs

Materials Needed

- tadpole kit (or tadpoles or frog
  eggs collected locally)
  A tadpole kit can be purchased
  from Home Science Tools at:
  www.hometrainingtools.com.
- aquarium
- water
- tadpole food

Objectives

In this unit students will observe a tadpole turning into an adult frog.

The objectives of this lesson are for students to:

- Make careful observations of the metamorphosis of a frog.
- Learn about a life cycle.

Experiment

I. Think About It

Read this section of the *Laboratory Notebook* with your students.

❶ Have the students think about how the frog got its name. Help them look up the origin of the name *frog* in a library or internet reference source.

Have the students make a drawing of how they think the frog got its name.

❷ Have the students think about how a tadpole turns into a frog. Help them explore their ideas with questions such as:

- *What do you think happens first when a tadpole changes to a frog?*
- *What do you think happens next when a tadpole changes to a frog?*
- *What do you think happens last when a tadpole changes to a frog?*
- *Do you think you can watch the tadpole as it changes to a frog?*
- *What do you think the tadpole will eat when it becomes a frog?*
- *What color do you think the adult frog will be?*

Have the students draw their idea of what will happen as a tadpole changes into a frog.

II. Observe It

Read this section of the *Laboratory Notebook* with your students.

Guide the students in setting up the tadpole kit. If you have collected tadpoles or frog eggs locally, you can find instructions for their care and feeding on the internet or at the library.

Help the students follow the directions included in the kit or obtained online.

For Step ❶: If students are beginning with tadpoles rather than frog eggs, have them find pictures of frog eggs online or at the library.

Have the students observe the growth of a tadpole into a frog. Help them make careful observations and drawings, noting how the tadpole changes.

III. What Did You Discover?

Read this section of the *Laboratory Notebook* with your students.

Have the students answer the questions about the life cycle of a frog. Help them write summary statements about what they actually observed. They may have expected something different to happen, but encourage them to record what actually did happen — even if the frogs did not grow, or the eggs or tadpoles died.

IV. Why?

Read this section of the *Laboratory Notebook* with your students.

Discuss any questions that might come up.

Help the students understand that the life cycle of a frog is a very amazing process. Have a discussion about the meaning of metamorphosis as it applies to the frog life cycle.

Explain to the students that scientists would not know about the life cycle of a frog if they did not make careful observations. In the same way, careful observations by the students showed them that a tadpole and a frog are the same creature. They also could see the changes that take place during metamorphosis.

V. Just For Fun

In this experiment students are asked to go outside and look for frogs, toads, lizards, snakes, birds, and fish in different stages of their life cycle. A trip could be taken to a nearby park, wooded area, aquarium, fish hatchery, zoo, or botanical garden.

Students are to make notes and drawings of their observations in their field notebook.

More REAL SCIENCE-4-KIDS Books
by Rebecca W. Keller, PhD

Building Blocks Series yearlong study program — each Student Textbook has accompanying Laboratory Notebook, Teacher's Manual, Lesson Plan, Study Notebook, Quizzes, and Graphics Package

Exploring the Building Blocks of Science Book K (Activity Book)
Exploring the Building Blocks of Science Book 1
Exploring the Building Blocks of Science Book 2
Exploring the Building Blocks of Science Book 3
Exploring the Building Blocks of Science Book 4
Exploring the Building Blocks of Science Book 5
Exploring the Building Blocks of Science Book 6
Exploring the Building Blocks of Science Book 7
Exploring the Building Blocks of Science Book 8

Focus Series unit study program — each title has a Student Textbook with accompanying Laboratory Notebook, Teacher's Manual, Lesson Plan, Study Notebook, Quizzes, and Graphics Package

Focus On Elementary Chemistry
Focus On Elementary Biology
Focus On Elementary Physics
Focus On Elementary Geology
Focus On Elementary Astronomy

Focus On Middle School Chemistry
Focus On Middle School Biology
Focus On Middle School Physics
Focus On Middle School Geology
Focus On Middle School Astronomy

Focus On High School Chemistry

Super Simple Science Experiments

21 Super Simple Chemistry Experiments
21 Super Simple Biology Experiments
21 Super Simple Physics Experiments
21 Super Simple Geology Experiments
21 Super Simple Astronomy Experiments
101 Super Simple Science Experiments

Note: A few titles may still be in production.

Gravitas Publications Inc.
www.gravitaspublications.com
www.realscience4kids.com

CPSIA information can be obtained
at www.ICGtesting.com
Printed in the USA
BVHW011630260320
575514BV00010B/47

9 781941 1813